I'm going to be a...

DANCER

AUTUMN
PUBLISHING

Published in 2021
First published in the UK by Autumn Publishing
An imprint of Igloo Books Ltd
Cottage Farm, NN6 0BJ, UK
Owned by Bonnier Books
Sveavägen 56, Stockholm, Sweden
www.autumnpublishing.co.uk

0821 001
2 4 6 8 10 9 7 5 3 1
ISBN 978-1-80022-261-8

Written by Suzanne Fossey
Illustrated by Junissa Bianda

Designed by Richard Sykes
Edited by Suzanne Fossey

Printed and manufactured in China

I'm going to be a...
DANCER

AUTUMN
PUBLISHING

When I grow up, I'm going to be a dancer!

I'll perform dance moves that
no one has ever tried and be the
best dancer anyone has ever seen!

My teacher will put on any type of music and I'll know exactly what to do.

When the music stops, I'll carry on dancing because I will be so good that the music will be in my head.

I'm going to have to be very good.

I'll go to lessons every week and practise every day.

The teacher will show me how to do all kinds of things,

from beautiful ballet to brilliant break-dancing.

You'll see me jumping...

... kicking my legs...

... and spinning in circles.

I'll cross the stage by flying through the air.

All of a sudden, I'll SPIN AROUND...

... leap up and land perfectly.

It will look spectacular!

I will learn to dance with lots
of people in a big group routine.

Crowds of people will turn up
just to watch me dance.

I'll dress in sparkly sequins and dance on the stage in a giant theatre. My parents will come to see me. EVERYONE will clap and shout,

"BRAVO!"

I'll dance in front of a camera, on a film set.

Someone will yell "CUT!" and the director will congratulate me.

They'll say, "You're going to be famous!"

I'll choose a glittery costume with lots of big, brightly coloured feathers.

I'll dance through the streets, leading a huuuuuuuuge parade that stretches for miles.

I'll set up my own dance studio and
make up my own routines.

People will queue up just to get in the door and I'll teach them everything I know.

When I grow up, I'll
do all these things.

But I've got lots of other things to do first.

BEING A DANCER

Dancers move around to music, creating beautiful art and using their bodies to tell stories. There are lots of different styles of dance, from ballet to ballroom, tap dancing, street dance and many more. Dancers go to classes to learn new moves. They put these moves together into routines that they practise again and again until they know them off by heart. They have to do lots of exercises to keep their bodies strong and flexible.

Dancers perform in all kinds of places.
Some dance on stage in front of big audiences, while others dance on TV or in films. Some dancers spend their time making up new routines and teaching them to others.
However and wherever you want to dance, the whole world is your stage!